101 BRAIN TEASERS & RIDDLES

FOR SMART KIDS

Welcome!

This book belongs to:

_____

Thank you for choosing our book: "101 Brain Teasers and Riddles for Smart Kids." It's great to see that you enjoy doing these activities as much as we do!

This is a big workbook! It was made for you to make sure you get to do all the activities you could ever want. It'll offer hours of entertainment and a refreshing way to both unplug and improve your brain functions through problem solving, and so much more!

101 BRAIN TEASERS AND RIDDLES FOR SMART KIDS

•••••• CONTENTS ••••••

Level 1

THE GREATEST MATH TEST

1 Incredible Sum

Sansa added **8 + 8 = 4**.
How is this possible?

2 Outstanding Number

The number
8,549,176,320 is an
outstanding number.
Do you know what
makes it special?

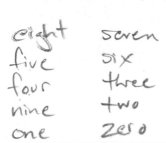

eight   seven
five   six
four   three
nine   two
one   zero

3 Substracting Numbers

What is the maximum possible number of times you can subtract number **5** from number **25**?

4 Kids in Classroom

There are **12** kids in a classroom. **6** kids are wearing **socks** and **4** kids are wearing **shoes.** **3** kids are wearing both **socks** and **shoes.** How many kids are **barefoot** in the classroom?

5 Positive Numbers

What are the three positive numbers that give the same result when multiplied together or added together?

6 Can You Help Jerry?

Using only **addition**, Jerry wants to use eight **number 8s** to get a total of **1,000.** Can you help him out?

7 Number Series

If 2 + 2 = **44**, 3 + 3 = **96**, 4 + 4 = **168**, 5 + 5 = **2510**. Then what is 6 + 6 = ? *6612*

8 What is the Number?

Jackson is trying to multiply this number by any other number, but the answer will always be the same. What is the number? *0*

9 A Matter of Minutes

How many minutes are in a quarter of an hour?

15

10 Buying Tomatoes

Tobey went to the grocery store to buy **12 tomatoes**. On his way home, all but **9** get mushed and ruined. How many tomatoes are left in good condition?

Level 2

TENSES CHALLENGES

11 Smartphone Dialing

If you multiply all of
the numbers on
the dial pad of a
smartphone, what
would the total be?

12 Building a Barn

If it took **8** people **10 hours**
to build a barn, how long
would it take **14**
people to build the
same barn?

13 The Empty Triangle

What number should
be placed in the empty
triangle?

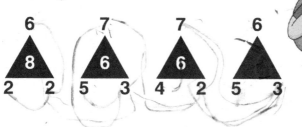

14 What is the Number?

Which one has **two
zero** and **two four**?

    A. 0044
    B. 2024
    C. 0024

15 The Next Number

What is the next number in the sequence? **2, 4, 8, 16...**

16 Sequential Numbers

1 = 3, 2 = 3, 3 = 5,
4 = 4, 5 = 4, 6 = 3,
7 = 5, 8 = 5, 9 = 4,
10 = ??

Can you complete the sequence?

17 Type of Number

Two even numbers added together always make an even number. An even number and an odd number added together always make an odd number. What type of number always comes from adding two odd numbers together?

18 Painting Numbers

Harry was asked to paint the number plates on **100** apartments, which means he will have to paint numbers **1** through **100**. Can you figure out the number of times he will have to paint the number **6**?

19 Great Number

What can you put between **5** and **6** to make the result greater than **5**, but less than **6**?

20 Josh's Wish

Josh wants to subtract the number **10** from **100**, How many times can he do that?

Level 3

LOGIC CHALLENGES

21 Guess What?

What has,

Cities, but no **Houses.**
It has **Forests**, but
no **Trees.** It has
Water, but no **Fish.**

22 Letter Sequence

What letter comes
next in the following
sequence?

D R M F S L T _

23 Month of the Year

During which **month** of the year do people sleep the least?

24 Mysterious Water

I am made up of **water,** but when you drop me into a bowl full of water, I will die. What am I?

25 Eating Apples

Five people were eating apples. **A** finished before **B**, but behind **C**. **D** finished before **E**, but behind **B**. What was the finishing order?

26 What Happens...?

What happens to **break,** yet never falls, and what **falls,** yet never breaks?

27 In Front of You

What is always at
the front of you
but can't be **seen**?

28 What Are They?

The more you
take ahead of
you, the more
you leave behind.
What are they?

29 Going to Bed

What is the last thing you take off before bed?

30 The Breakfast

Jellybean loves to eat; a lot! But she can never eat two things for breakfast: what are they?

Level 4

UNSOLVABLE RIDDLES

31 An Even Number

X is an odd number. Take a letter away from **X** and it becomes an **even number**. Which is that number?

32 What Am I?

I am a **three-digit** number. My second digit is **4** times bigger than the **third** digit. My **first** digit is **3** less than my **second** digit. What am I?

33 Center of Gravity

What sits at the center of **Gravity**?

34 Wrong Spelling

The only single word that is spelled **incorrectly** in the dictionary is_____?

35   Make Me Bigger

The more you take from me, the bigger I get. What am I?

36   The Seed

I am a **seed**. I am spelt using only three letters. Take away two letters and I sound quite the same. What am I?

37 The Strangers

I can let you see strangers through the wall, but if you are careless, I can allow a stranger into your house. What am I?

38 Keys Without Door

I have a lot of **keys** but not a single door. There is **space** but no rooms. I can allow you to **enter** but you can never leave. What am I?

39 Animals on the Ark

How many animals altogether did **Moses** take on the ark?

40 The Fifth Child

Billy's mother had five children. The first was named **Lala**, the second was named **Lele**, the third was named **Lili**, the fourth was named **Lolo**. What was the **fifth child** named?

Level 5

THE CRYPTIC ANSWER

41 The Planets

You can find it in **Mercury**, **Earth**, **Mars**, **Jupiter** and **Saturn**, but not in **Venus** or **Neptune**. What is it?

42 Rings Without Fingers

What has many rings but no fingers at all?

43 The Third Son

Matthew's father had three sons: Peter, John and...?

44 Mrs. Wilson's Children

Mrs. Wilson has two children. If the oldest child is a girl, what are the odds that the other child is also a girl?

45 Good Company

If two is a company and three is a crowd, what are four **and** five?

46 Crazy Operation

How can you take **2** from **5** and leave **4**?

47 Sides of a Circle

How many sides does a **circle** have?

48 Always Late

What is never **present** and always appears to be **late**?

49 Your Hands

What can you hold in your **Left hand,** but not in your **Right hand?**

50 The Dark Room

Old granny Linda walks into a dark room with a Matches box, a Candle, a Kerosene Lamp, and a Fireplace. Which one does she light first?

Level 6

MIND-BLOWING RIDDLES

51 At the Grocery

Jane bought an object at the grocery but she had to break it before she could use it. What object did you have to **break** before you were able to use it?

52 It Belongs to You

What personally belongs to you but your friends use it more than you?

53 What is the Item?

Larry is holding a piece of an item; it has a **head** and a **tail** but it has no body. What is the item?

54 Days of the Month

Some months have 31 days, some have 30 days. What month has 28 days?

55 The Question

What question can you never answer **YES** to?

56 Wet and Dry

What becomes **wetter** the more it **dries**?

57 The Greenhouse

If **red** houses are made of red bricks, and **yellow** houses are made of yellow bricks, what is a **green**house made of?

58 Matter of Time

Mr. Darius rode into a town on **Friday** and stayed in a hotel. Two nights later he rode home on **Friday**. How is this possible?

59 The Letter T

What begins with **T**, finishes with **T**, and has **T** in it?

60 The Daughters

Elizabeth has four daughters: Diva, Angel, Daisy and Adeline, and each of her daughters has a brother — how many children does Elizabeth have?

Level 7

THE SURREAL DISCOVERY

61 The White House

Mr. Blue lives in the **blue house**, Mr. Yellow lives in the **yellow house**, and Mr. Black lives in the **black house**. Who lives in the **white house**?

62 The Deserts

SAG is a Mnemonic to help you remember the three largest deserts in the world. What are they?

63 Our Solar System

Can you name the eight planets in our solar system closest to the sun? Here is a hint; *"My Very Excellent Mum Just Served Us Noodles"*

64 A Seven Letter Word

What is a **seven** letter word containing dozens of letters?

65 A Pink Story

In a **one-story pink** house, there was a **pink** person, a **pink** cat, a **pink** computer, a **pink** chair, a **pink** table, a **pink** telephone– everything in the house was **pink**! What color were the stairs?

66 Under an Umbrella

If Josh, his sister Lizzy, and their dog weren't under an umbrella, why didn't they get wet?

67 Playing with Textbook

Jack was playing with a textbook and he mistakenly tore out pages 7 and 8, 100 and 101, 222 and 223. How many pages did Jack tear out in total?

A. 6   B. 4   C. 7   D. 5   E. 3

68 The Apples

Lady Bluebell has **four** apples. She took away **three.** How many does she have left?

69 It Becomes Smaller

What becomes smaller when you turn it upside down?

70 The Truck Driver

Mr. Benjamin, who is a truck driver, is going opposite the traffic on a one-way street. A police officer sees him but doesn't stop him. Why didn't the police officer stop Mr. Benjamin?

Level 8

DIFFICULT MIND PUZZLES

71 A Great Invention

What great invention lets you look right through a wall?

72 At The Restaurant

Two **mothers** and two **daughters** went out to eat at the restaurant. Everyone ate one burger, yet only **three** burgers were eaten in all. How is this possible?

73 Guess What I am?

Can you guess what I am? I'm at the beginning of **eternity** and the end of **time** and space. I'm at the beginning of every end and the **end** of every **place**. What am I?

74 Black and White

I am black and white and am carried and read all over the world, can you guess what I am?

75 The End of Everything

What is the end of **everything**?

76 Can You See It?

What is something you never see again?

77 The Alphabet

Why is the alphabet shorter during the Christmas season?

78 Say My Name

I disappear the moment you say my name. What am I?

79 The Great King

I am known as a **king**. The jungle is where I reign. It's hard to tame me. And I have a large mane. What am I?

80 The Race

Bonny, Quinn and Xander are running a race. **Xander** is at first place, **Bonny** is at second position while **Quinn** is at third position. If **Quinn** runs ahead of the **second person** in the race, what position is Quinn in?

Level 9

THE BIG DILEMMA

81 The Traveler

I look like a city wall from afar. Up close I look like a row of houses. I do not stay in one place but travel thousands of miles. What am I?

82 What is It?

It keeps running but it has no legs. It makes a mighty sound but it has no voice. It always falls down but it can never move up. What is it?

83 The Strongest

I am one of the lightest things on earth, but even **Hulk,** who is the strongest person in the world, cannot hold me for more than five minutes. What am I?

84 Sharing Knowledge

I can share a lot of knowledge but I have no voice. I can be **opened** and **closed**, but I am not a **door**. What am I?

85 Think About It

What is it that when you take the **whole** of it, **some** remains?

86 Multiple Color

What has white, green, red, blue, brown, purple, black, and orange in it?

87 The Homework

When is homework not homework?

88 The Number One

How do you make the **number one** go away without subtraction or division?

89 Mr. Mustard

Mr. Mustard is a **Tennis player** and a **Cook.** There is one thing he serves but he can never **eat**. What is it?

90 Nothing to Say

My voice is tender, my waist is slender and I'm often invited to play. Yet wherever I go I must take my bow or else I have nothing to say. What am I?

Level 10

WORD COMBINATIONS

91 Special Words

What is special about the following words: **Revive, Grammar, Potato, Dresser, Banana?**

92 A Four Letter Word

What **4-letter** word can be written **forward** or **backward** and can still be read from **right** to **left**?

93 English Alphabet

How many letters are there in **the English alphabet**?

94 The Next Letter

What Letter Is Next In This Sequence: **O, T, T, F, F, S, S,**?

95   **What Word Am I?**

I am a **word** of **three letters**. Add two letters to me and fewer there will be. What word am I?

96   **Crazy Time**

What comes once in a minute, twice in a moment, but never in a thousand years?

97 Thousands of Letters

What starts with a **P**, and ends with an **E** and it also contains **thousands** of letters in it?

98 You Love to Eat It

I have seven letters and I am something you always love to eat. If you remove my first 3 letters, I become an adjective or a noun and removing my first 4 letters, leaves a measure of time. What am I?

99 Animal Meeting

What do **Dogs**, **Cats**, **Birds**, **Goats**, and **Fish** all have in common?

100 An English Word

What English word has **five** letters but sounds like it only has **one** letter?

101 Letter Series

Guess the next three letters in the series **GTNTL**.

Level 1 THE GREATEST MATH TEST

1 ## Incredible Sum

When you think in terms of TIME.
8AM + 8 hours = 4PM.

2 ## Outstanding Number

This is the only **number** that includes all the **digits** arranged in an **alphabetical order.**

3 ## Substracting Numbers

Only once. This is because when you subtract **5** from **25** for the first time, it then becomes the number **20**, then **15, and so on.**

4 ## Kids in Classroom

As we know **3** kids are wearing both, so only **3** kids are wearing only **socks (6 - 3 = 3)** and **1** kid is wearing only **shoes (4 - 3 = 1).** So, in total, **3 + 3 + 1 = 7.** Now we have 12 kids there, so **12 - 7 = 5.** So, there are only **5 kids** that are barefoot.

5 Positive Numbers

The numbers are: **1, 2 and 3.**

6 Can You Help Jerry?

Here it is: **888 +88 +8 +8 +8 =1,000**

7 Number Series

The answer is **3612**. It is the number multiplied by itself and then the number added to itself. Six multiplied by six is **36**, and six plus six is **12. Putting those two together, you get 3612!**

8 What is the Number?

The number is **ZERO!**

9 A Matter of Minutes

There are **15 minutes** in a quarter of an hour.

10 Buying Tomatoes

There are **9** tomatoes left in good condition.

11 Smartphone Dialing

The result will be **ZERO.** Since the numbers **0** thru **9** are represented on a dial pad, any number multiplied by zero equals zero.

12 Building a Barn

None — That same barn is already built!

13 The Empty Triangle

3 is the right answer. The top number minus the bottom left-hand number is multiplied by the bottom right-hand number to give the number inside the triangle.

6
3
5   3

14 Looking for Numbers

The correct option is **B (2024),** as we write "two zero two four" as 2024. 0044 cannot be the answer as it would be written as "zero zero four four" and 0024 would be written as "zero zero two four."

15 The Next Number

32— the formula is doubling the previous number.

16 Sequential Numbers

10 = 3. The number after the equal sign refers to the number of letters in the number before the equal sign.

17 Type of Number

An **Even** number!

18 Painting Numbers

20 times. (6, 16, 26, 36, 46, 56, 60, 61, 62, 63, 64, 65, 66, 67, 68, 69, 76, 86 and 96).

19 Great Number

A decimal point. Your result would be **5.6**, which is between **5** and **6**.

20 Josh's Wish

He can only do that once, because when he subtracts it the first time, the number is no longer **100** (it's 90!).

Level 3 — LOGIC CHALLENGES

21 Guess What?

The answer is a **MAP.**

22 Letter Sequence

D is the answer. Each letter represents one note in the diatonic musical scale: **Do, Re, Mi, Fa, Sol, La, Ti, Do.**

23 Month of the Year

February (there are usually **fewer nights** in February).

24 Mysterious Water

An **ICE-CUBE.**

25 Eating Apples

CABDE. Putting the first three in order, **A** finished in front of **B** but behind **C**, so **CAB.** Then, we know **D** finished before **B**, so **CABD.** We know **E** finished after **D**, so **CABDE.**

Brain Teasers Answers

26 ## What Happens...?
The answer is **Morning** and **Night**.

27 ## In Front of You
It's the **Future!**

28 ## What Are They?
Your **Footsteps!**

29 ## Going to Bed
Your feet off the **Floor.**

30 ## The Breakfast
They are **Lunch** and **Dinner!**

Level 4 UNSOLVABLE RIDDLES

31 ## An Even Number
The answer is **Seven** (take away the letter "s" from seven and it is "even").

Brain Teasers Answers

32 What Am I?
The number is **141**.

33 Center of Gravity
The letter **'V'** sits at the center of the word Gravity.

34 Wrong Spelling
The word is **"INCORRECTLY"**

35 Make Me Bigger
It is a **HOLE!**

36 The Seed
The seed is a **PEA!**

37 The Strangers
It is a **window!**

38 Keys Without Door
It is a **computer Keyboard**.

39 Animals on the Ark

Moses didn't take anything on the ark. **Noah** did all that!

40 The Fifth Child

The name of the fifth child is **"Billy"**

Level 5 THE CRYPTIC ANSWER

41 The Planets

The Letter **'R'**

42 Rings Without Fingers

A **TELEPHONE!**

43 The Third Son

The name of the third son is **MATTHEW!**

44 Mrs. Wilson's Children

50 percent. Since you can only give birth to either a boy or a girl.

Brain Teasers Answers

45 ## Good Company
The answer is **9.**

46 ## Crazy Operation
The answer is **F I V E.** Remove the 2 letters **F** and **E** from five and you have **IV** (the roman numeral for 4!).

47 ## Sides of a Circle
The circle has **TWO** sides: the **inside** and the **outside.**

48 ## Always Late
The answer is the word "**LATER!**"

49 ## Your Hands
Your **Right Elbow!**

50 ## The Dark Room
The Matches in the Box.

Brain Teasers Answers

51 At the Grocery
The object is an **EGG!**

52 It Belongs to You
The answer is your **NAME!**

53 What is the Item?
The item is a **COIN!**

54 Days of the Month
All the 12 months in the calendar have 28 days.

55 The Question
The question is: **'Are you asleep yet?'**

56 Wet and Dry
The answer is a **'Towel.'**

57 The Greenhouse

They are made of **Glass**; all greenhouses are made up of **Glass**.

58 Matter of Time

Friday is the name of Mr. Darius' horse. He rode on his horse to the town and to his home.

59 The Letter T

The answer is **TEAPOT**!

60 The Daughters

Elizabeth has **Five** children; each daughter has the same brother.

Level 7 — THE SURREAL DISCOVERY

61 The White House

The **President** of the United States.

62 The Deserts

Sahara, Arabian, and Gobi.

Brain Teasers Answers

63 Our Solar System

Mercury, Venus, Earth, Mars, Jupiter, Saturn, Uranus, Neptune.

64 A Seven Letter Word

The answer is a **Mailbox!**

65 A Pink Story

There weren't any stairs in the house, it was a **one-story** house.

66 Under an Umbrella

They didn't get wet because it wasn't **raining.**

67 Playing with Textbook

The correct answer is **E (3).** When you rip out a sheet from a book, you're tearing out a numbered page on each side of the piece of paper.

68 The Apples

If Lady Bluebell took three Apples, then of course she only has **3** Apples.

69 ## It Becomes Smaller
The number Nine **(9)**.

70 ## The Truck Driver
Mr. Benjamin was not driving, he was **Walking!**

Level 8 DIFFICULT MIND PUZZLES

71 ## A Great Invention
The invention was the **Window!**

72 ## At The Restaurant
It's only possible because they were a **grand-mother**, a **mother**, and her **daughter**.

73 ## Guess What I am?
I'm the letter **E!**

74 ## Black and White
The **NEWSPAPER!**

Brain Teasers Answers

75 **The End of Everything**
The letter **g**.

76 **Can You See It?**
Yesterday!

77 **The Alphabet**
The Christmas alphabet has no **L (NOEL)**.

78 **Say My Name**
The answer is **Silence.**

79 **The Great King**
LION, because I'm the king of the Jungle.

80 **The Race**
Quinn is now in the **second** position.

Level 9 THE BIG DILEMMA

81 **The Traveler**
The **Train!**

Brain Teasers Answers

82 What is It?
A **Waterfall!**

83 The Strongest
The **Air** we **Breathe.**

84 Sharing Knowledge
The answer is a **Book.**

85 Think About It
The word "**Wholesome.**"

86 Multiple Color
A box of **Crayons!**

87 The Homework
When you get to do it in **Class!**

88 The Number One
Just add the letter **G** to "**One**" to make it "**Gone**"

89 Mr. Mustard
A **Tennis ball.**

90 Nothing to Say

I am the **Violin!**

Level 10 **WORD COMBINATIONS**

91 Special Words

Take the **first** letter of each word and place it at the end. It will spell the same word **backwards.**

92 A Four Letter Word

The answer is **NOON.**

93 English Alphabet

The answer is **18.**

94 The Next Letter

The letter "**E**". They are all the first letters of the numbers spelled in order.

O – One	**F** – Five
T – Two	**S** – Six
T – Three	**S** – Seven
F – Four	**E** – Eight

95 What Word Am I?
The word is **FEW!**

96 Crazy Time
The letter **M.**

97 Thousands of Letters
The **Post office.**

98 You Love to Eat It
The answer is **SAUSAGE!**

99 Animal Meeting
The letter "**S.**"

100 An English Word
The word is **Queue**.

101 Letter Series
I, T, S. The complete sequence is the first letter of every word in the sentence.

CONGRATULATIONS

Excellent work! I am sure that there were some obstacles along the way, but you persisted and fi nished the activities! Hooray!

I also want to give a HUGE THANKS to our staff at Kids Castle Press for making these books a reality. It wouldn't have been possible without them. Feel free to visit our website below to show them some love!

In addition, if you'd like us to send you more free content to print out, you can do so by visiting our website: www.kidscastlepress.com.

To add a cherry on top... You can email us for a chance to win a free physical copy of our next book. info@kidscastlepress.com.

Don't miss out as we won't be doing this forever... it's a limited time only!

Lastly, if you like this book, would you be so kind as to drop me a review on Amazon?

Thank you very much!

Jennifer L. Trace

- -

 **ACTIVITY PRO CERTICATE**

_____

Date: _____   Signed: _____

Made in the USA
Coppell, TX
06 March 2022

74505186R00046